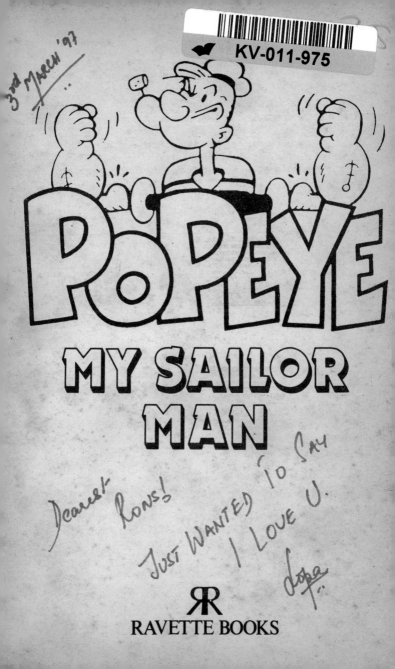

First published by
Ravette Books Limited 1989

Printed and bound in Great Britain
for Ravette Books Limited,
3 Glenside Estate, Star Road, Partridge Green,
Horsham, West Sussex RH13 8RA
by Cox & Wyman Ltd, Reading

ISBN 1 85304 193 9

TM

6-1

6-3

6-11

7-4

7-21

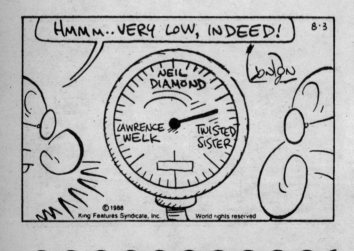

8-30

London

9-16

RAVETTE CARTOON CLASSICS